Level K

Mathematics
3rd Edition

Nancy McGraw and Joan Archer

Bright Ideas Press, LLC
Cleveland, OH

Summer Solutions Level K

Mathematics
3rd Edition

Printed in the United States of America

United States coin images from the United States Mint.

ISBN: 978-1-60873-261-6

Cover Design: Dan Mazzola
Editor: Randy Reetz

Instructions for Parents / Guardians

- *Summer Solutions* is an extension of the *Simple Solutions* Approach being used by thousands of children in schools across the United States.

- The 30 lessons included in each workbook are meant to review and reinforce the skills learned in the grade level just completed.

- The program is designed to be used three days per week for ten weeks to ensure retention.

- Completing the book all at one time defeats the purpose of sustained practice over the summer break.

- Each book contains answers for each lesson.

- Each book also contains Help Pages which list vocabulary, solved examples, formulas, and measurement conversions.

- Lessons should be checked immediately for optimal feedback. Items that were difficult for students or done incorrectly should be resolved to ensure mastery.

- Adjust the use of the book to fit vacations. More lessons may have to be completed during the weeks before or following a family vacation.

Summer Solutions
Mathematics K

Reviewed Skills Include:

- Sort Objects by Shape, Size, and Color

- Spatial Relationships

- Relative Position of Objects: Under, Over, Inside, Outside, Beside, etc.

- Represent, Read, and Order Numbers 0–20

- Use a Number Line

- Find Missing Numbers in a Sequence

- Identify and Sort 2- and 3-Dimensional Figures

- Units of Time and Tell Time to the Hour

- Use a Calendar

- Identify Money: Penny, Nickel, Dime

- Compare Objects of Different Lengths, Weights, and Capacities

- Use Comparative Terms: Longer, Shorter, Heavier, Lighter, More, Fewer, Greater, Less Than, Equal To

- Add to Numbers 0–9

- Subtract from Numbers 0–10

Help Pages begin on page 63.

Answers to Lessons begin on page 73.

Lesson #1

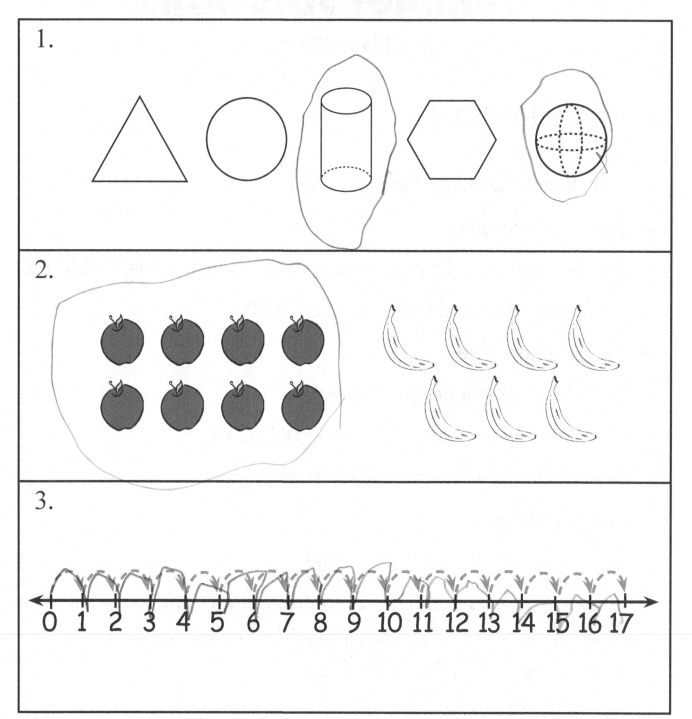

Directions:

1. Color the **three-dimensional** shapes.

2. Count the objects in each group. Which group is **greater**? Circle it.

3. Trace the lines as you count up to 17.

4.

_____
5 ¢
_____

5.

_____
11 o'clock
_____

6.

$4 + 0 =$ ___ $2 + 2 =$ ___

$3 + 1 =$ ___ $3 + 2 =$ ___

Directions:

4. Write the number of cents.

5. Write the time shown on the clock.

6. Write the sums.

Lesson #2

1.

___ + ___ = 3   ___ + ___ = 3

2.

		June				
S	M	T	W	T	F	S
	1	2	3	4	5	6
7	8	9	10	11	12	13
14	15	16	17	18	19	20
21	22	23	24	25	26	27
28	29	30				

————————
- - - - - - -
————————

3.

————————
- - - - - - -
————————

Directions:

1. There are different ways to make a sum of 3. Finish the number sentences.

2. Circle every Monday. Use a blue marker. Count the number of Mondays. Write the number.

3. Count the dinosaurs. How many are there? Write the number.

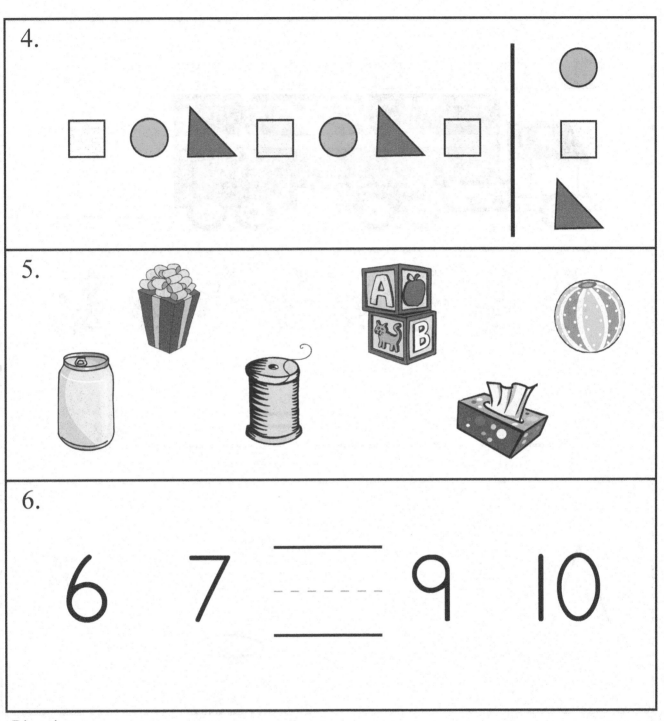

Directions:

4. Circle the shape that should come next in the pattern.

5. Circle the objects that can roll.

6. Write the missing number.

Lesson #3

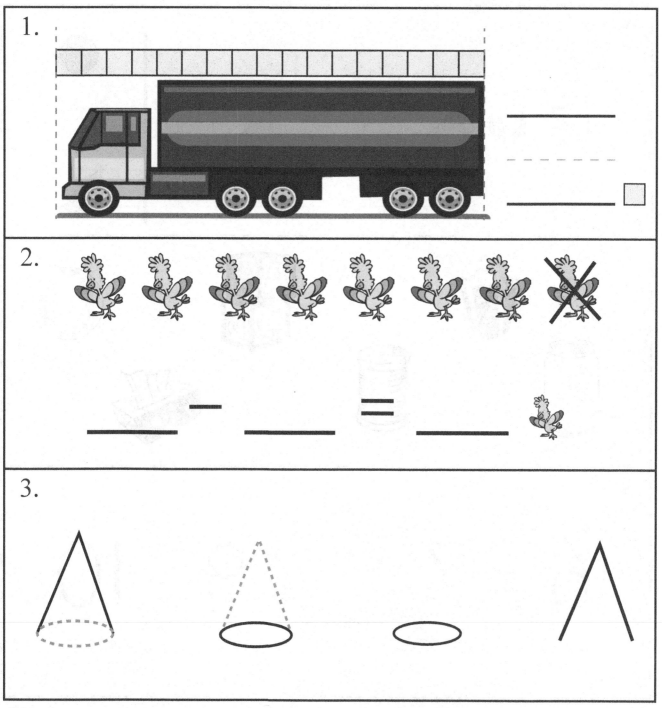

Directions:

1. How many squares long is the truck? Write the number on the line.

2. There were 8 birds. 1 flew away. How many birds are left? Fill in the number sentence.

3. Trace the lines to complete the first two cones. Draw the missing parts of the last two cones.

4.

5.

6.

Directions:

4. Circle the **smallest** triangle.

5. Circle the picture that shows the bird **above** the tree.

6. Circle the object that is **heavier**.

Lesson #4

1.

_____
- - - - - ¢
_____

2.

16

3.

_____
- - - - - o'clock
_____

Directions:

1. Write the number of cents.

2. Trace the number 16. Count the objects in each group. Circle the group that has 16.

3. Write the time shown on the clock.

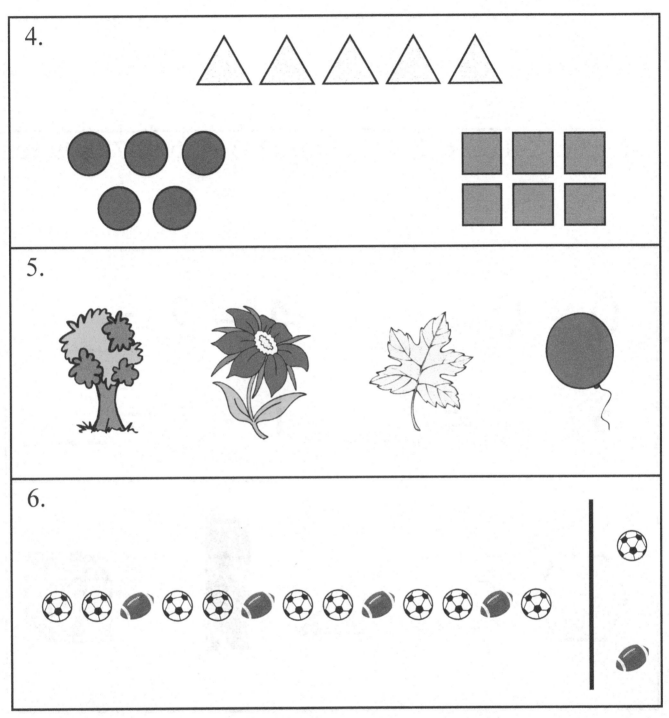

Directions:

4. Count the triangles. Which group is **equal to** the group of triangles? Circle it.

5. Circle the object that does <u>not</u> belong.

6. Circle the object that should come next in the pattern.

Lesson #5

1.

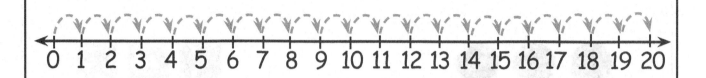

0 1 2 3 4 5 6 7 8 9 10 11 12 13 14 15 16 17 18 19 20

2.

$0 - 0 = \underline{\hspace{1cm}}$ $4 - 2 = \underline{\hspace{1cm}}$

$3 - 1 = \underline{\hspace{1cm}}$ $1 - 1 = \underline{\hspace{1cm}}$

3.

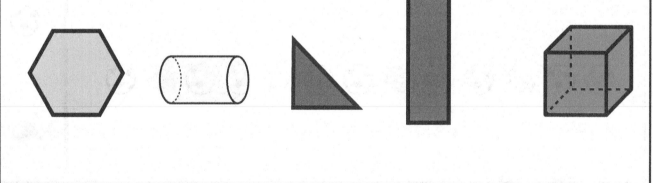

Directions:

1. Trace the lines as you count up to 20.

2. Write the differences.

3. Circle the **two-dimensional** shapes.

4.

_____
- - - - - - -
_____

5.

October						
S	**M**	**T**	**W**	**T**	**F**	**S**
				1	2	3
4	5	6	7	8	9	10
11	12	13	14	15	16	17
18	19	20	21	22	23	24
25	26	27	28	29	30	31

6.

2   3   4   ___   6

Directions:

4. There are 5 yellow leaves and 5 green leaves. How many leaves in all? Write the number on the line.

5. Circle every Thursday. Use a red marker. Circle the first Sunday. Use a blue marker.

6. Write the missing number.

Lesson #6

1.

2.

$$\_+\_=7 \qquad \_+\_=7$$

3.

Directions:

1. Circle the picture that shows the bowl **on** the table.

2. There are many ways to make a sum of 7. Finish the number sentences.

3. Circle the object that holds **more**.

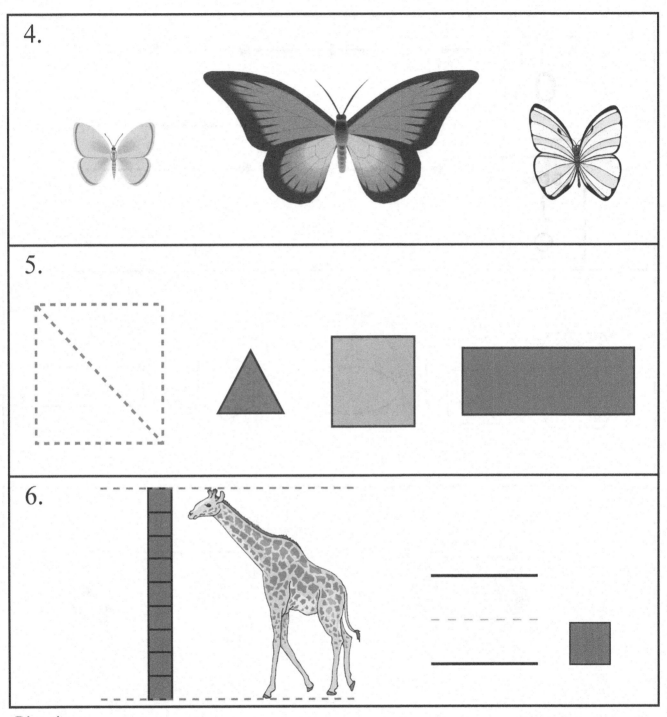

Directions:

4. Circle the **smallest** butterfly. Put an X on the **largest** butterfly.

5. Trace the dotted lines. What shape can be made from 2 triangles?

6. How many squares tall is the giraffe? Write the number on the line.

Lesson #7

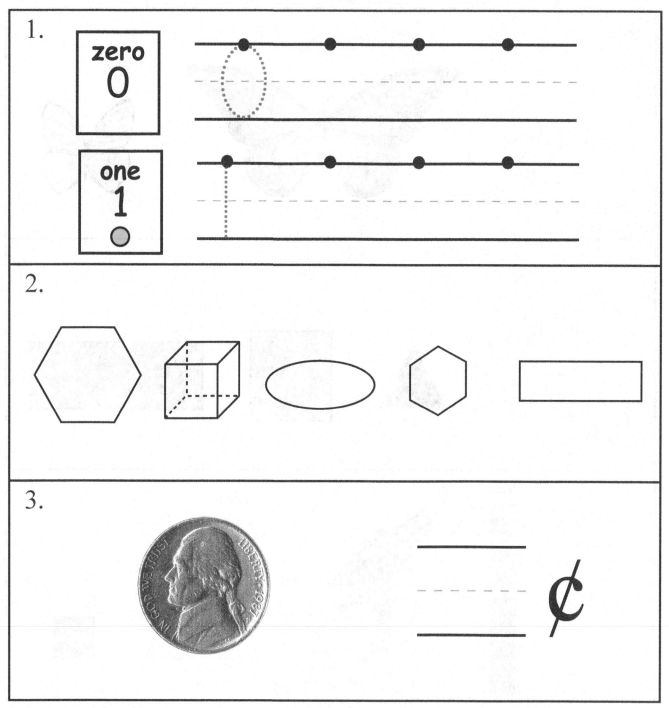

Directions:

1. Trace the numbers 0 and 1. Write each number 3 more times.

2. Color the hexagons.

3. Write the number of cents.

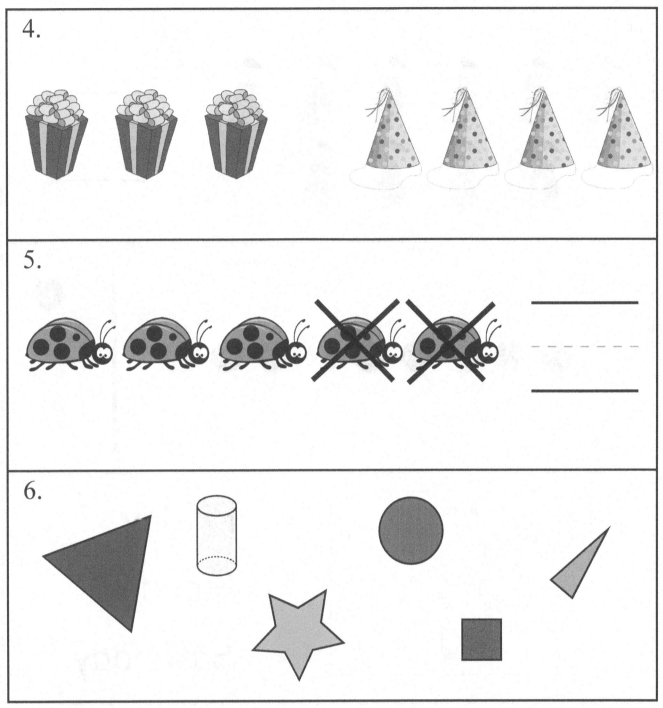

4.

5.

6.

Directions:

4. Count the objects in each group. Which group is **less than** the other? Circle it.

5. There are 5 ladybugs. 2 ladybugs fly away. How many ladybugs are left? Write the number on the line.

6. Circle the shapes that have three corners.

Lesson #8

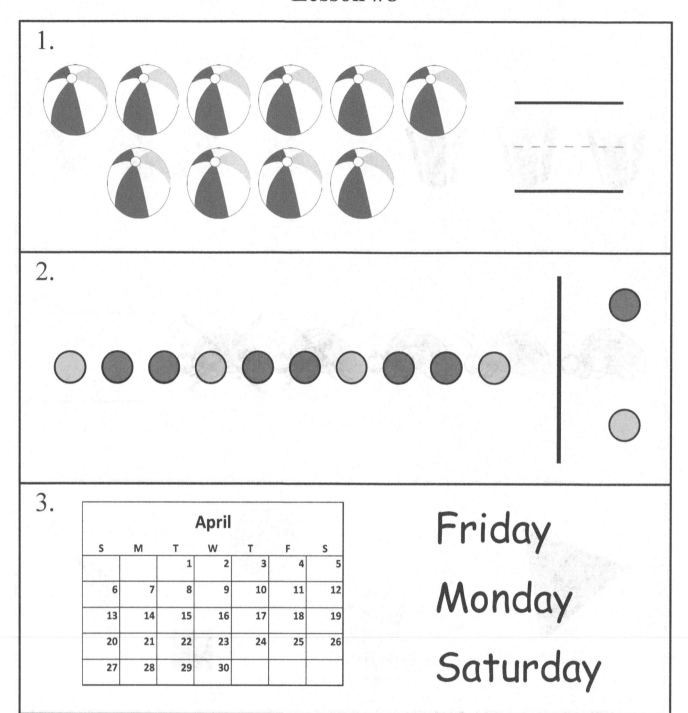

Directions:

1. Count the balls. How many are there? Write the number.

2. Circle the object that should come next in the pattern.

3. Circle the day of the week that April 5ᵗʰ falls on.

4.

$$1 + 1 = \underline{} \qquad 2 + 0 = \underline{}$$

$$1 + 3 = \underline{} \qquad 2 + 3 = \underline{}$$

5.

6.

 $\underline{}$ o'clock

Directions:

4. Write the sums.

5. Count the objects in each group. Circle the group that has **more**.

6. Write the time shown on the clock.

Lesson #9

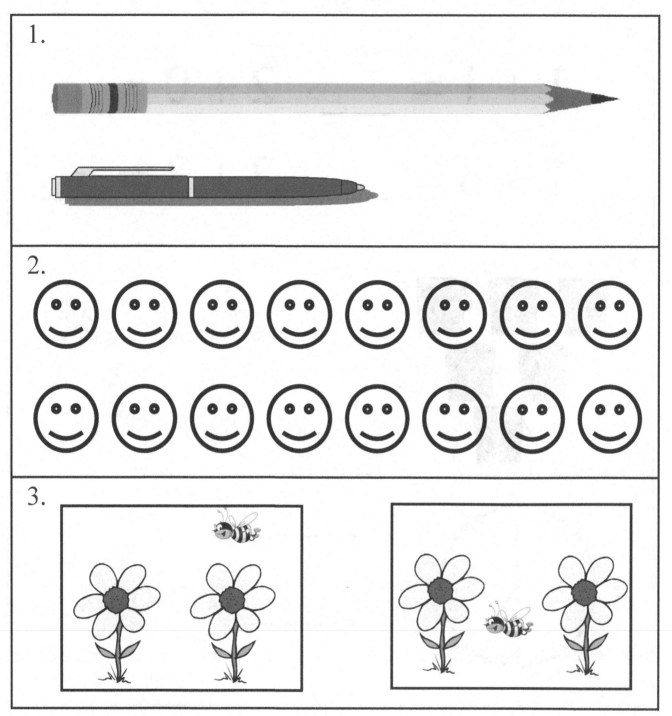

Directions:

1. Circle the object that is **shorter**.

2. Color 13 smiley faces.

3. Circle the picture that shows the bee **between** the flowers.

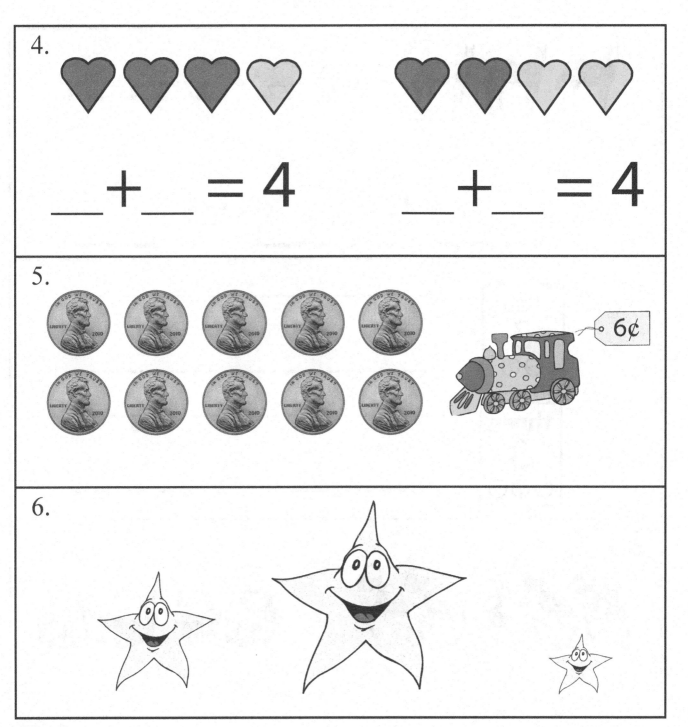

Directions:

4. There are many ways to make a sum of 4. Finish the number sentences.

5. Circle the pennies you need to buy the train.

6. Circle the object that is **biggest**. Put an X on the object that is **smallest**.

Lesson #10

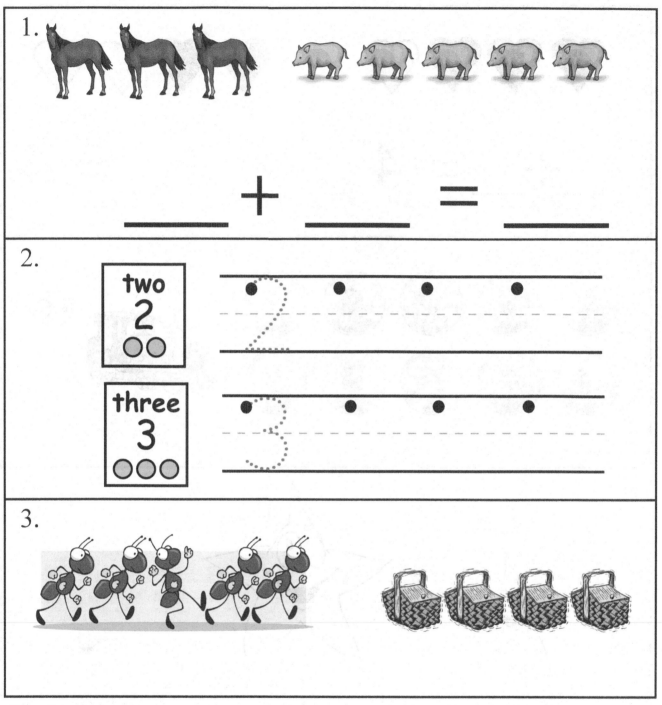

Directions:

1. There are 3 horses and 5 pigs on the farm. How many animals are there in all? Fill in the number sentence.

2. Trace the numbers 2 and 3. Write each number 3 more times.

3. Count the objects in each group. Which group is **greater**? Circle it.

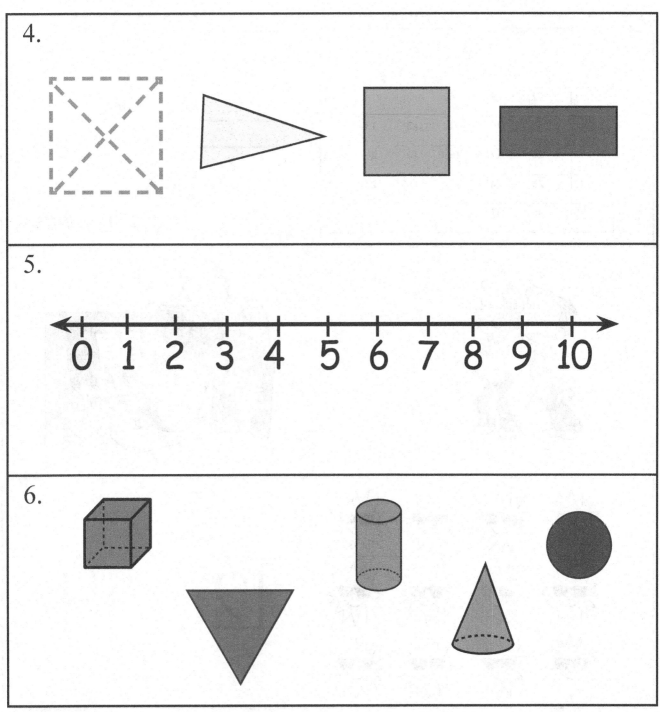

4.

5.

6.

Directions:

4. Trace the dotted lines. What shape can be made from 4 triangles? Circle the shape.

5. Circle the number that comes **before** 7.

6. Circle the **three-dimensional** shapes.

Lesson #11

1.

July

S	M	T	W	T	F	S
1	2	3	4	5	6	7
8	9	10	11	12	13	14
15	16	17	18	19	20	21
22	23	24	25	26	27	28
29	30	31				

_____ Sundays

_____ days in a week

2.

3.

12   14

Directions:

1. Circle every Sunday. Use a red marker. Write the number of Sundays. Count the number of days in one week.

2. Circle the activity that takes **longer**, practicing piano or blowing a bubble.

3. Count the suns. How many are there? Circle the number.

4.

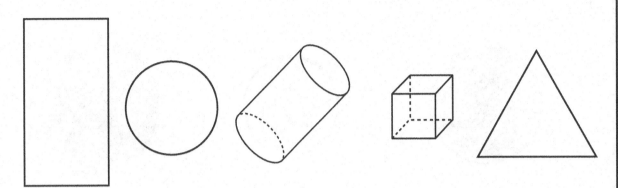

5.

6.

$3 - 2 =$ ___ $2 - 2 =$ ___

$1 - 0 =$ ___ $4 - 1 =$ ___

Directions:

4. Color the shapes that do <u>not</u> have corners.

5. Circle the object that should come next in the pattern.

6. Write the differences.

Lesson #12

1.

2.

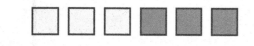

$\_\_ + \_\_ = 6$ $\_\_ + \_\_ = 6$

$\_\_ + \_\_ = 6$

3.

Directions:

1. Circle the dime.

2. There are many ways to make a sum of 6. Finish the number sentences.

3. Color 9 elephants.

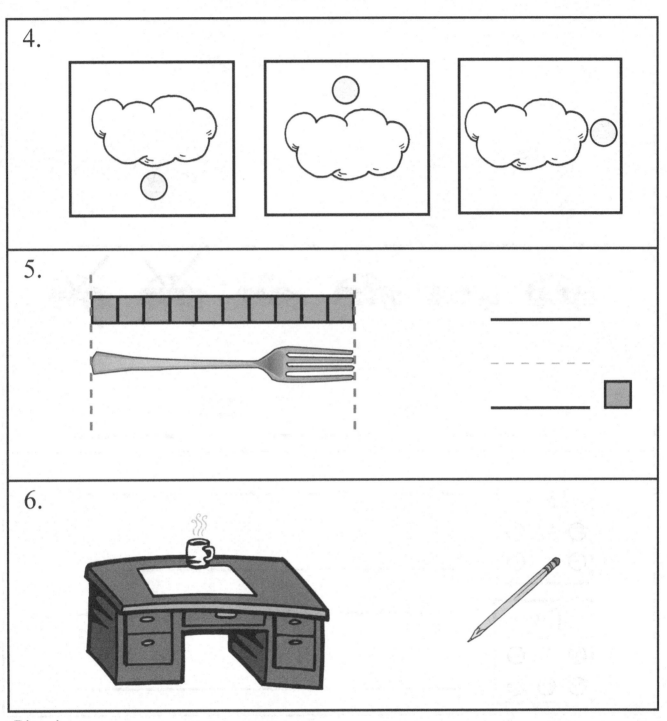

Directions:

4. Circle the picture that shows the circle **under** the cloud.

5. How many squares long is the fork? Write the number on the line.

6. Circle the object that is **lighter**.

Lesson #13

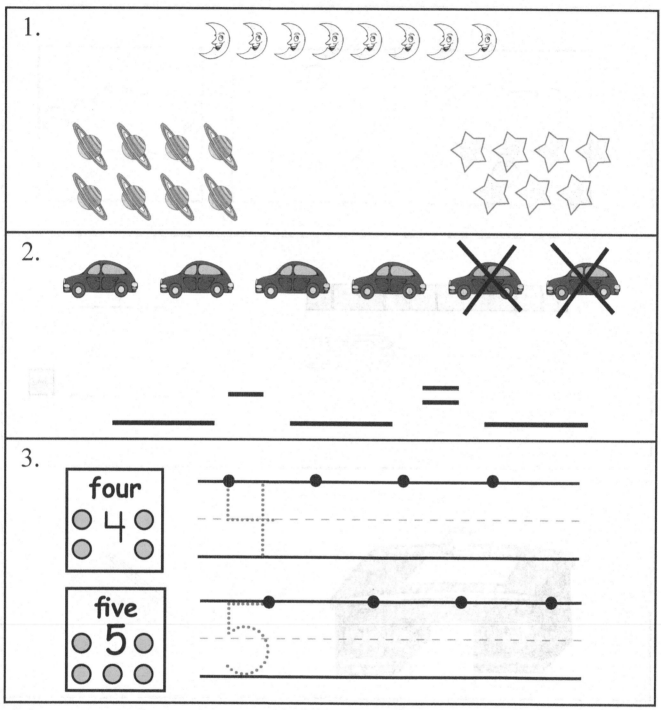

Directions:

1. Count the moons. Which group is **equal to** the group of moons? Circle it.

2. There were 6 cars. 2 drove away. How many cars are left? Fill in the number sentence.

3. Trace the numbers 4 and 5. Write each number 3 more times.

Directions:

4. Circle the objects that are in the shape of a cone.

5. Circle the object that is **shortest**. Put an X on the object that is the **tallest**.

6. Write the missing numbers.

Lesson #14

1.

_____
_____ o'clock

2.

3.

$0 + 3 = \underline{\quad}$ $2 + 1 = \underline{\quad}$

$1 + 0 = \underline{\quad}$ $0 + 0 = \underline{\quad}$

Directions:

1. Write the time shown on the clock.

2. Trace the dotted lines. What shape can be made from 2 squares? Circle the shape.

3. Write the sums.

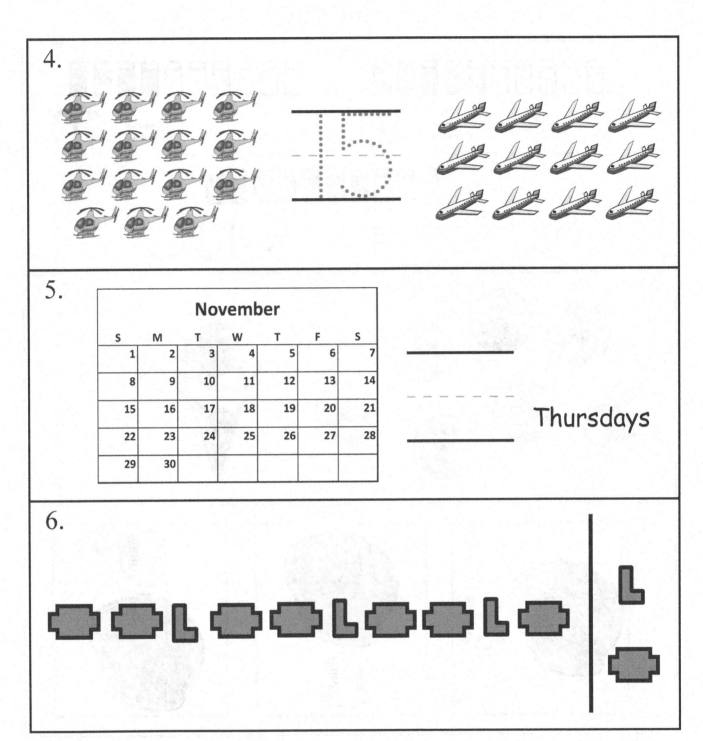

Directions:

4. Trace the number 15. Count the objects in each group. Circle the group that has 15.

5. Circle every Thursday. Use a red marker. Write the number of Thursdays.

6. Circle the object that should come next in the pattern.

Lesson #15

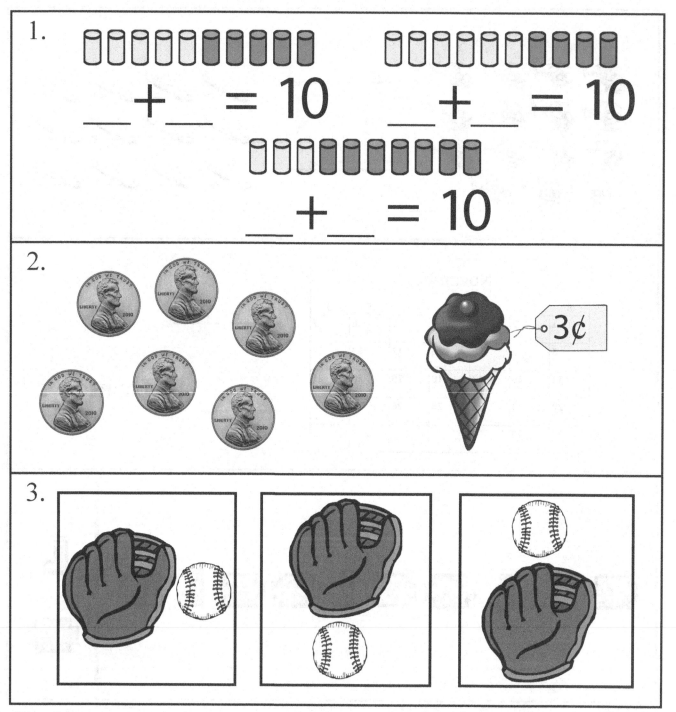

1. $\underline{\quad} + \underline{\quad} = 10$ $\underline{\quad} + \underline{\quad} = 10$

$\underline{\quad} + \underline{\quad} = 10$

2.

3.

Directions:

1. There are many ways to make a sum of 10. Finish the number sentences.

2. Circle the pennies you need to buy the ice cream.

3. Circle the picture that shows the ball **beside** the mitt.

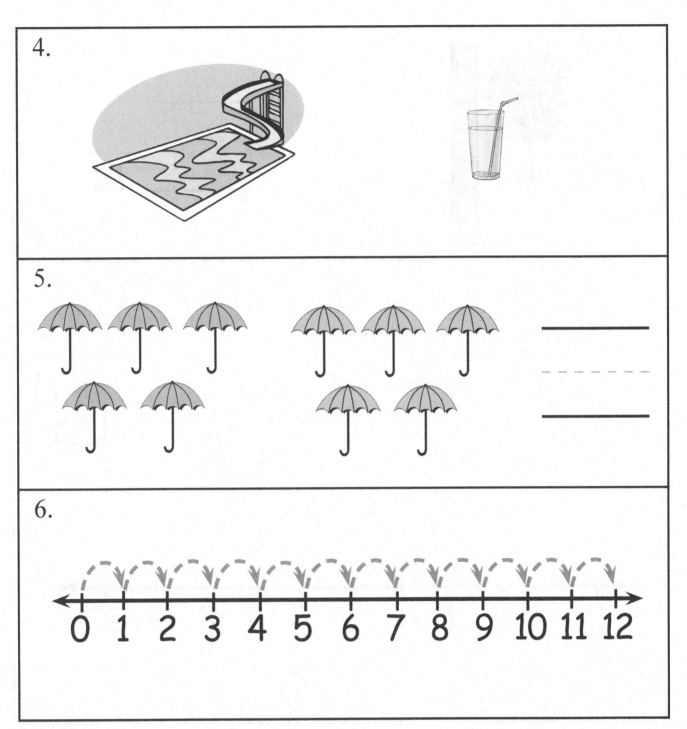

Directions:

4. Circle the object that holds **less**.

5. There are 5 pink umbrellas and 5 green umbrellas. How many umbrellas in all? Write the number on the line.

6. Trace the lines as you count up to 12.

Lesson #16

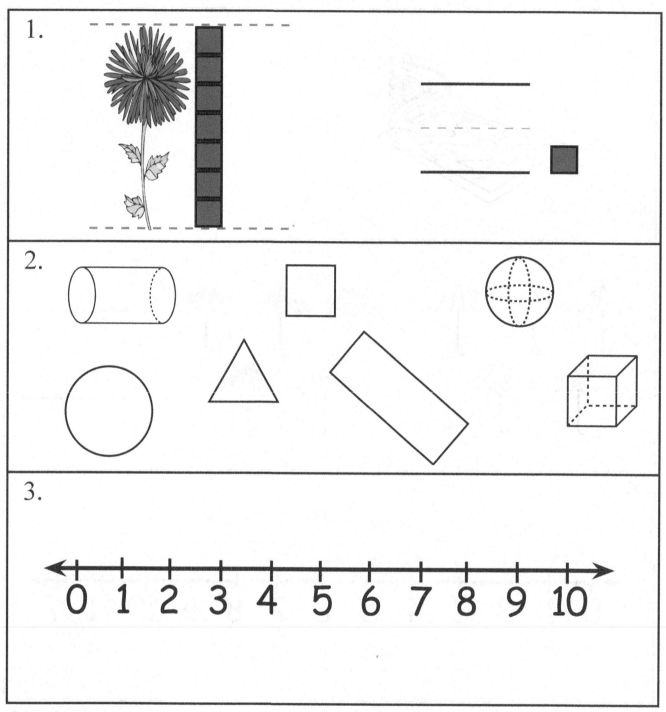

Directions:

1. How many squares tall is the flower? Write the number on the line.

2. Color the **two-dimensional** shapes.

3. Circle the number that comes after 0.

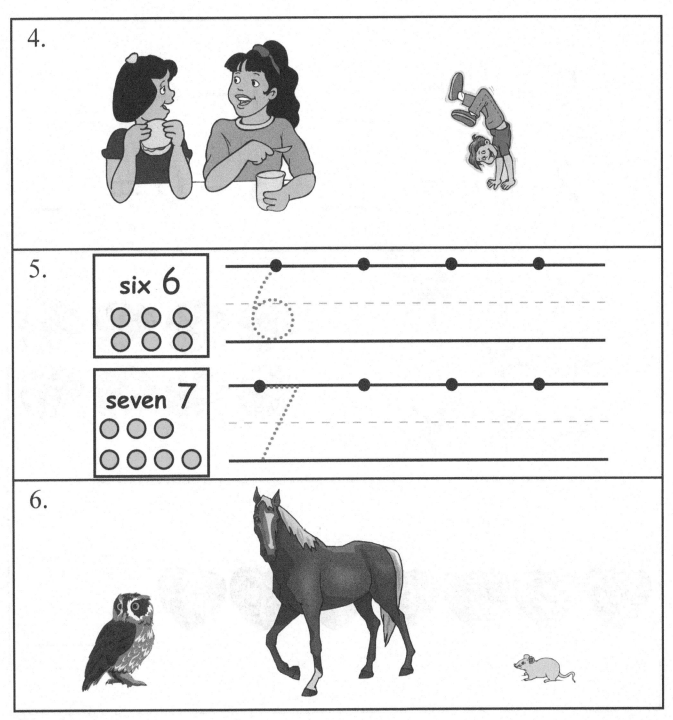

Directions:

4. Circle the activity that takes **less** time, eating lunch or doing a handstand.

5. Trace the numbers 6 and 7. Write each number 3 more times.

6. Circle the **smallest** animal. Put an X on the **largest** animal.

Lesson #17

1.

$$5 - 3 = \underline{\quad} \qquad 4 - 4 = \underline{\quad}$$

$$2 - 1 = \underline{\quad} \qquad 3 - 0 = \underline{\quad}$$

2.
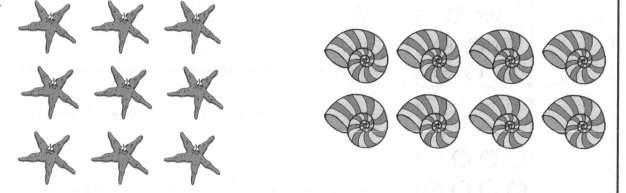

3.

Directions:

1. Write the differences.

2. Count the objects in each group. Which group is **less than** the other? Circle it.

3. Count the hearts. How many are there? Write the number.

4.

			August			
S	M	T	W	T	F	S
1	2	3	4	5	6	7
8	9	10	11	12	13	14
15	16	17	18	19	20	21
22	23	24	25	26	27	28
29	30	31				

_____ Wednesdays

_____ days in a week

5.

6.

Directions:

4. Circle every Wednesday. Use a green marker. Write the number of Wednesdays. Count the number of days in one week.

5. There are 10 balloons. 8 float away. How many balloons are left? Fill in the number sentence.

6. Trace the dotted lines. What shape can be made from 2 triangles? Circle the shape.

Lesson #18

1.

2.

3.

Directions:

1. Circle the coin that is worth 5¢.

2. Circle the object that should come next in the pattern.

3. Circle the object that does <u>not</u> belong.

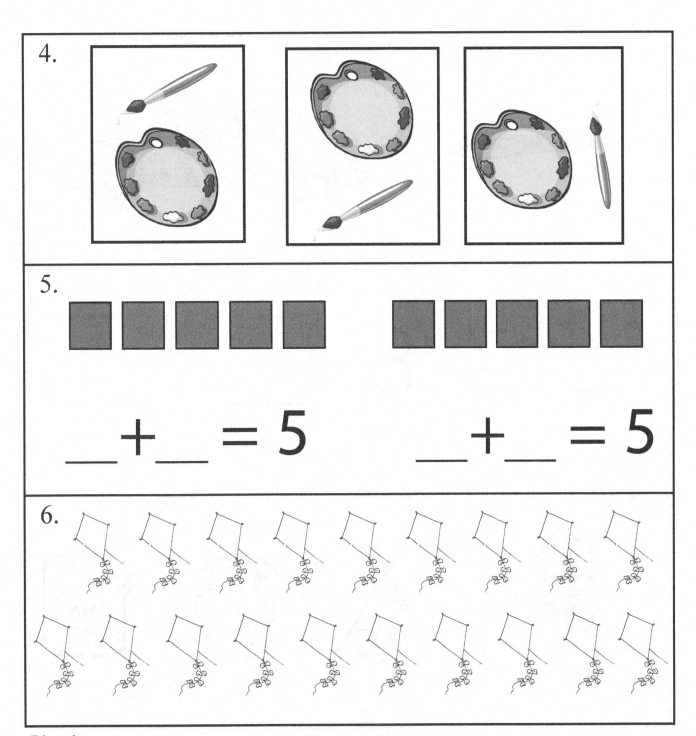

Directions:

4. Circle the picture that shows the paint brush **below** the palette.

5. There are different ways to make a sum of 5. Finish the number sentences.

6. Color 16 kites.

Lesson #19

1.

2.

$$6 \quad 7 \quad 8$$

3.

cylinder

Directions:

1. Circle the object that is **lighter**.

2. Write the missing numbers.

3. Circle the object that is in the shape of a cylinder.

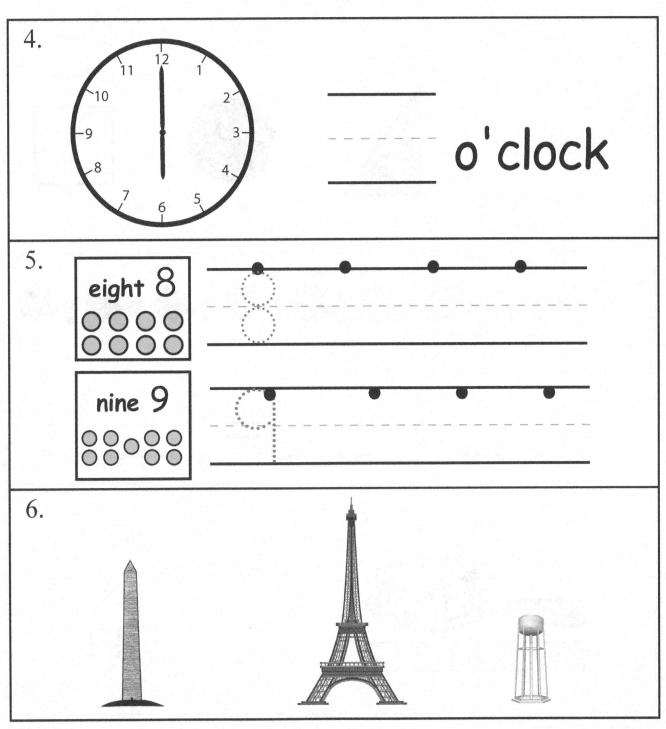

4. _____ o'clock

5. eight 8

nine 9

6.

Directions:

4. Write the time shown on the clock.

5. Trace the numbers 8 and 9. Write each number 3 more times.

6. Circle the **tallest** object.

Lesson #20

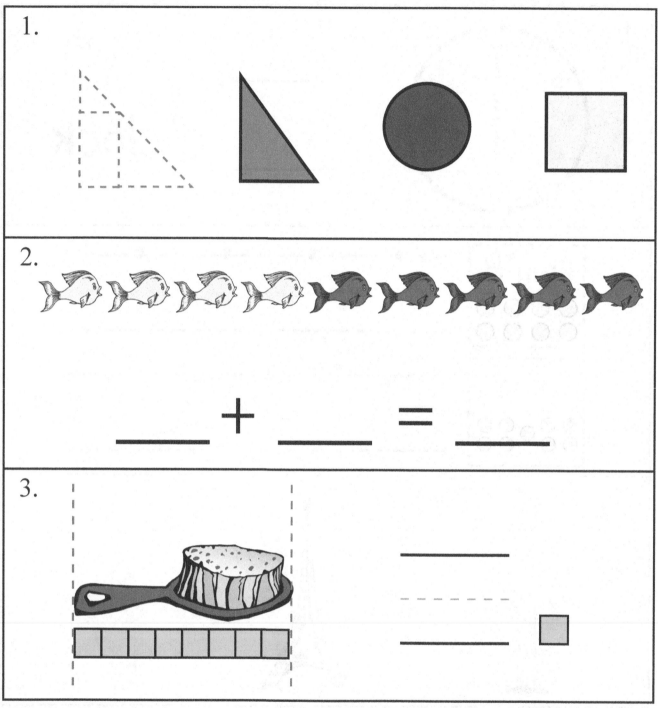

Directions:

1. Trace the dotted lines What shape can be made from a rectangle and 2 triangles? Circle the shape.

2. Sam and Jen went fishing. Sam caught 4 fish. Jen caught 5 fish. How many fish did they catch in all? Fill in the number sentence.

3. How many squares long is the brush? Write the number on the line.

4.

$$1 + 1 = \underline{\hspace{1cm}}$$ $$1 + 4 = \underline{\hspace{1cm}}$$

$$0 + 5 = \underline{\hspace{1cm}}$$ $$1 + 2 = \underline{\hspace{1cm}}$$

5.

			February			
S	M	T	W	T	F	S
	1	2	3	4	5	6
7	8	9	10	11	12	13
14	15	16	17	18	19	20
21	22	23	24	25	26	27
28						

_____ Fridays

_____ Saturdays

6.

   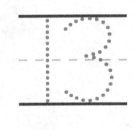   

Directions:

4. Write the sums.

5. Circle every Friday. Use a red marker. Circle every Saturday. Use a blue marker. Write the number of Fridays and Saturdays.

6. Trace the number 13. Count the objects in each group. Circle the group that has 13.

Lesson #21

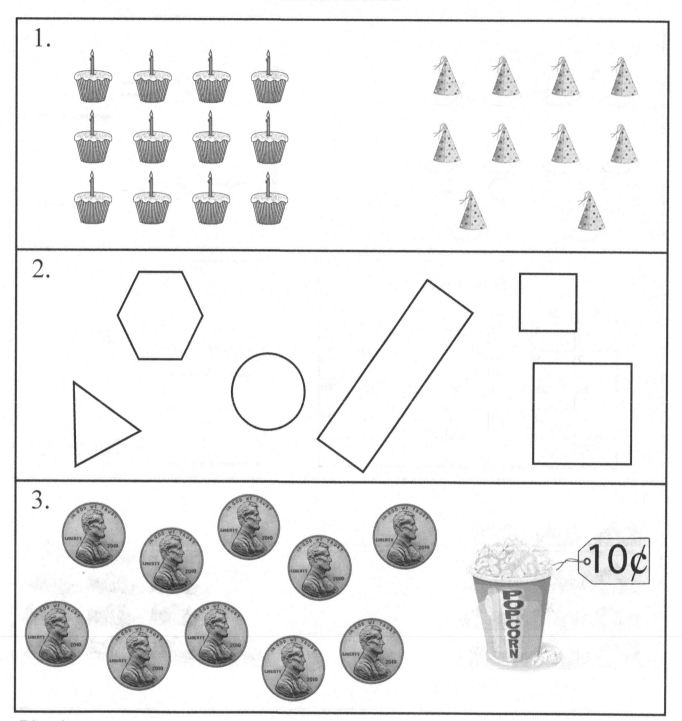

Directions:

1. Count the objects in each group. Which group is **greater**? Circle it.

2. Color the shapes that have 4 sides.

3. Circle the pennies you need to buy the popcorn.

4.

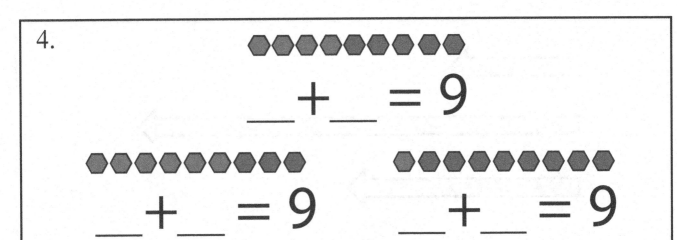

$$\_\_ + \_\_ = 9$$

$$\_\_ + \_\_ = 9 \qquad \_\_ + \_\_ = 9$$

5.

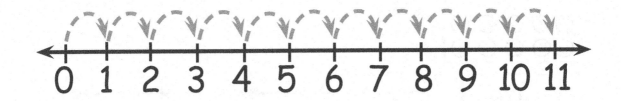

6.

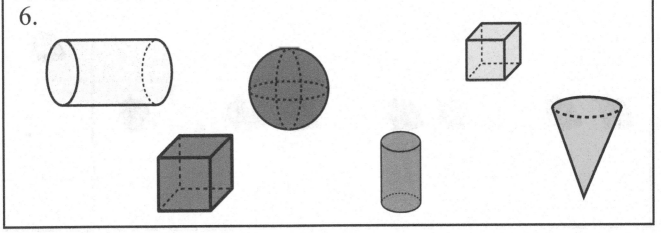

Directions:

4. There are many ways to make a sum of 9. Finish the number sentences.

5. Trace the lines as you count up to 11.

6. Circle the **three-dimensional** shapes.

Lesson #22

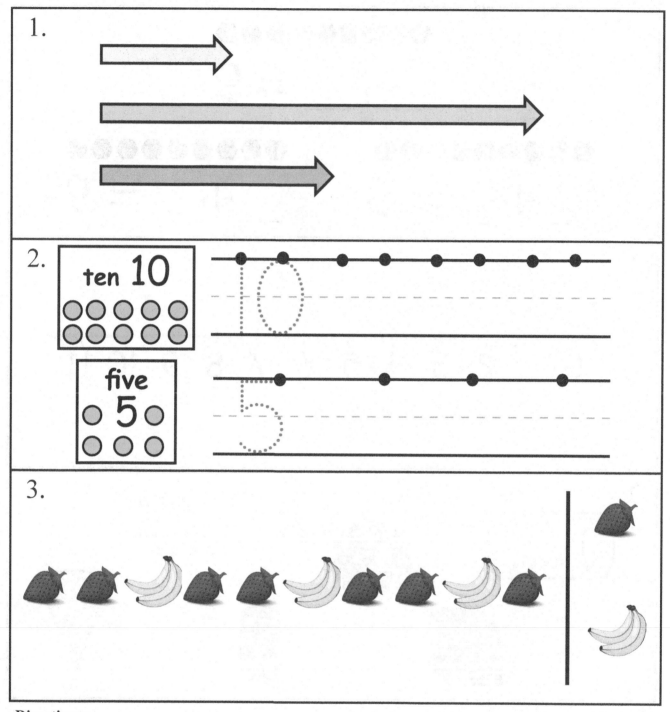

Directions:

1. Circle the object that is **longest**. Put an X on the object that is the **shortest**.

2. Trace the numbers 10 and 5. Write each number 3 more times.

3. Circle the object that should come next in the pattern.

4.

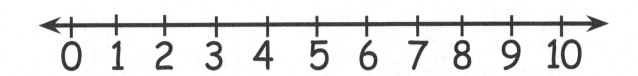

5.

6.

Directions:

4. Circle the number that comes **before** 10.

5. There are 8 pears. 4 pears are eaten. How many pears are left? Write the number on the line.

6. Circle the activity that takes **longer**, tying a shoe or reading a book.

Lesson #23

1.

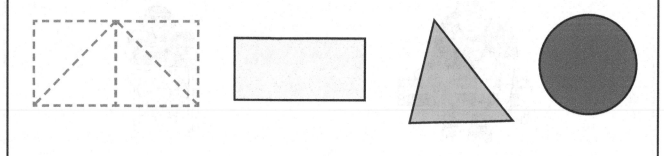

16   20

2.

$$3 - 3 = \underline{}$$ $$4 - 3 = \underline{}$$

$$3 - 2 = \underline{}$$ $$5 - 5 = \underline{}$$

3.

Directions:

1. Count the shells. How many are there? Circle the number.

2. Write the differences.

3. Trace the dotted lines. What shape can be made from 4 triangles? Circle the shape.

4.

March

S	M	T	W	T	F	S
		1	2	3	4	5
6	7	8	9	10	11	12
13	14	15	16	17	18	19
20	21	22	23	24	25	26
27	28	29	30	31		

Mondays

5.

6.

Directions:

4. What month does the calendar show? Write the name of the month. Circle every Monday. Use a red marker. Write the number of Mondays.

5. How many squares tall is the flamingo? Write the number on the line.

6. Circle the object that is **longer**.

Lesson #24

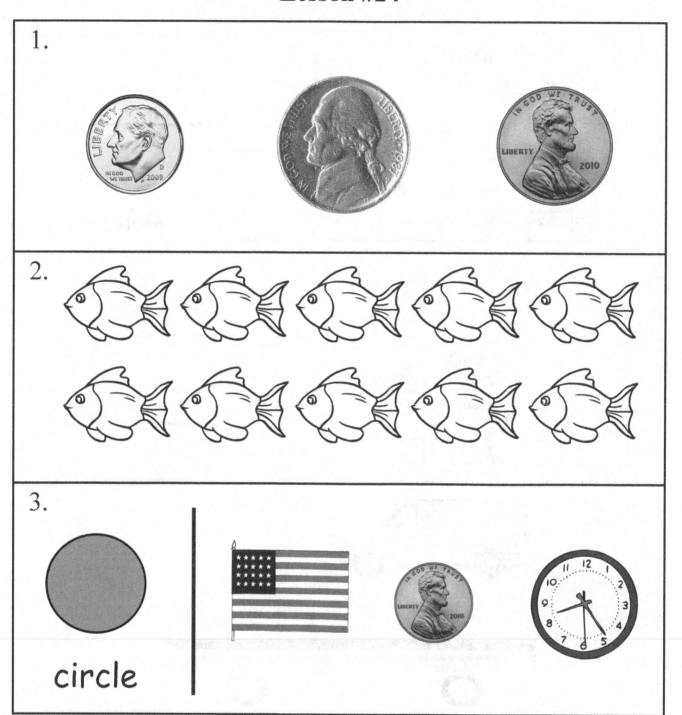

Directions:

1. Circle the coin that is worth 10¢.

2. Color 10 fish.

3. Circle the objects that are in the shape of a circle.

4.

5.

6.

Directions:

4. Circle the animal that is **behind** the elephant.

5. Circle the object that does <u>not</u> belong.

6. Count the objects in each group. Circle the group with **fewer**.

Lesson #25

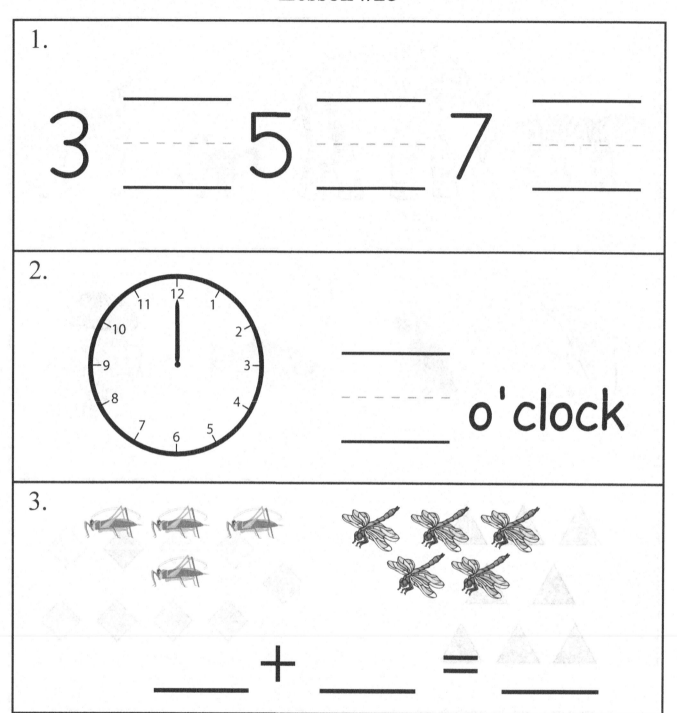

1.

3 _____ 5 _____ 7 _____

2.

_____ o'clock

3.

___ + ___ = ___

Directions:

1. Write the missing numbers.

2. Write the time shown on the clock.

3. There are 4 grasshoppers and 5 dragonflies. How many insects are there in all? Fill in the number sentence.

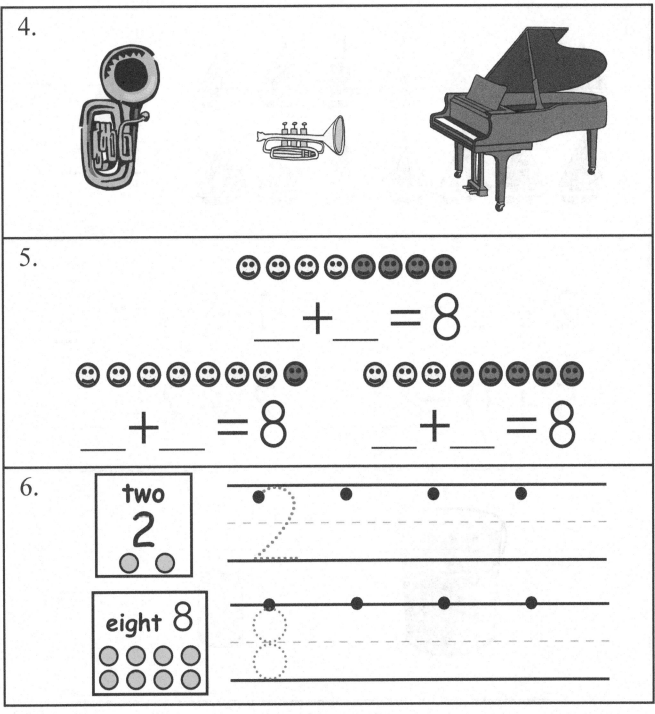

Directions:

4. Circle the object that is **biggest**. Put an X on the object that is **smallest**.

5. There are many ways to make a sum of 8. Finish the number sentences.

6. Trace the numbers 2 and 8. Write each number 3 more times.

Lesson #26

1.

_____

_____

2.

$2 + 3 =$ ___ $1 + 3 =$ ___

$5 + 0 =$ ___ $2 + 2 =$ ___

3.

Directions:

1. Count the boats. How many are there? Write the number.

2. Write the sums.

3. Circle the object that holds **more**.

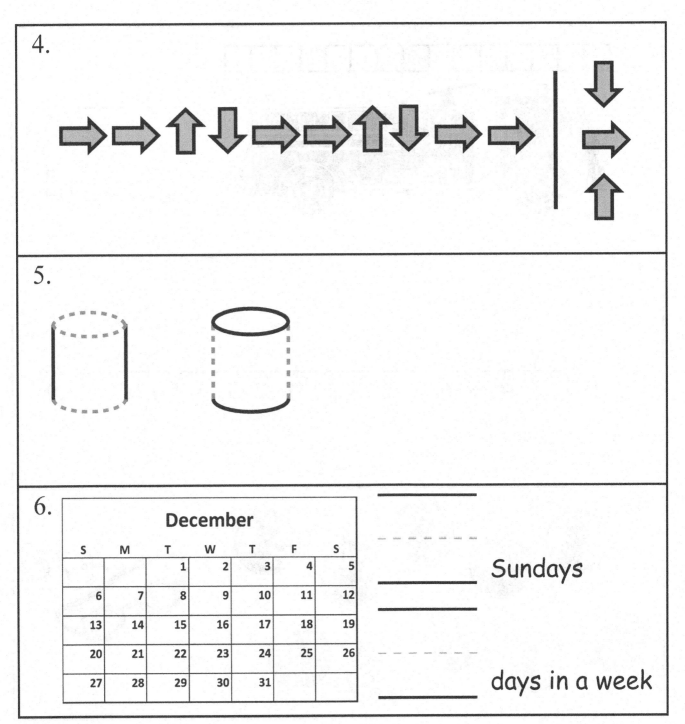

4.

5.

6.

December						
S	M	T	W	T	F	S
		1	2	3	4	5
6	7	8	9	10	11	12
13	14	15	16	17	18	19
20	21	22	23	24	25	26
27	28	29	30	31		

Sundays

days in a week

Directions:

4. Circle the object that should come next in the pattern.

5. Trace the lines to complete the cylinders. Then draw 2 more cylinders.

6. Circle every Sunday. Use a red marker. Write the number of Sundays. Count the number of days in one week.

Lesson #27

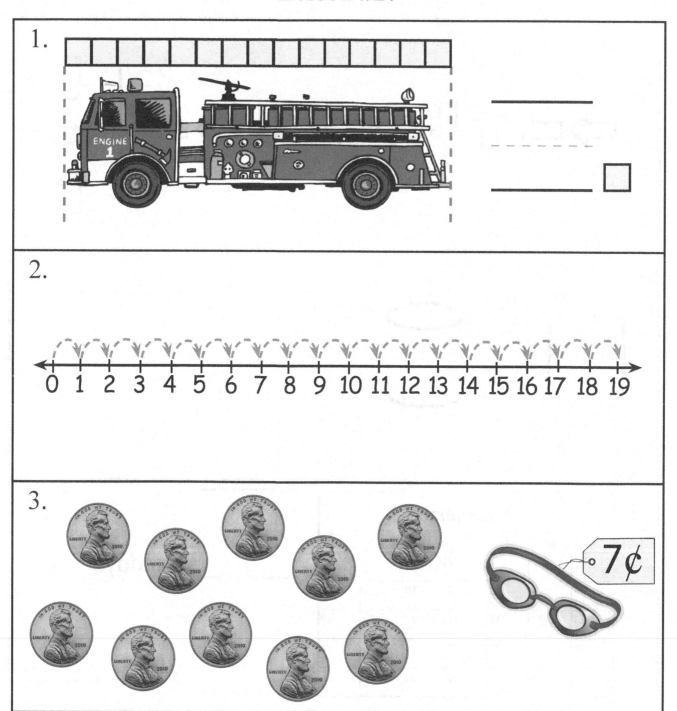

Directions:

1. How many squares long is the fire truck? Write the number on the line.

2. Trace the lines as you count up to 19.

3. Circle the pennies you need to buy the goggles.

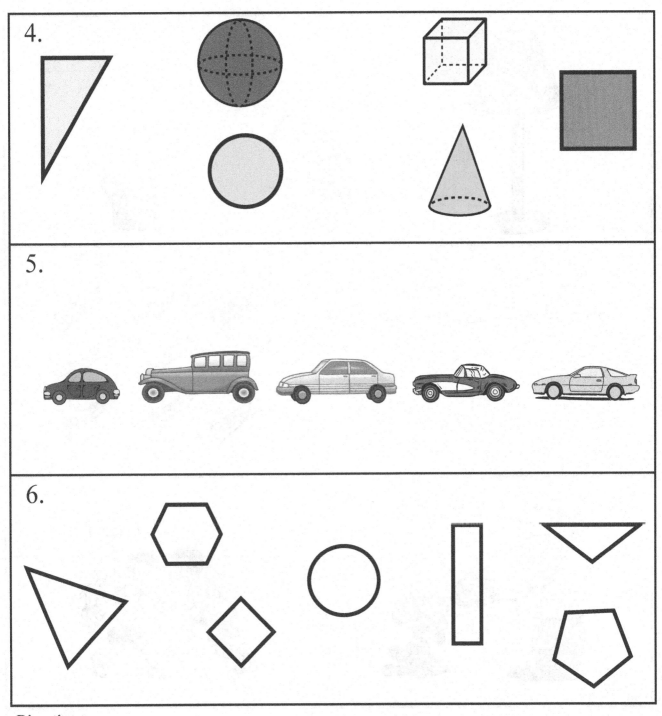

4.

5.

6.

Directions:

4. Circle the **two-dimensional** shapes.

5. Circle the car that is **in front of** the green car.

6. Color the shapes that have **more** than 3 corners.

Lesson #28

Directions:

1. Circle the object that is **shortest**. Put an X on the object that is the **tallest**.

2. Count the objects in each group. Circle the group with **more**.

3. Circle the activity that takes **less** time, feeding the dog or playing a basketball game.

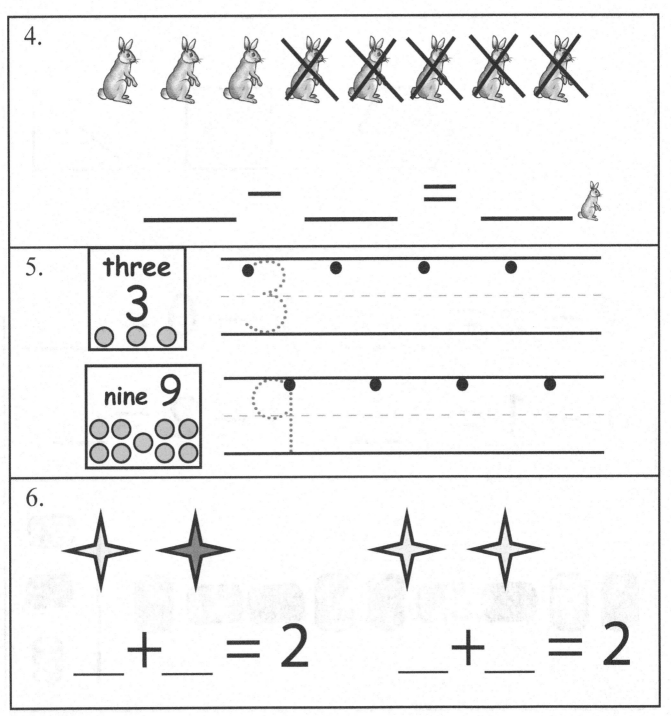

4.   ___ − ___ = ___

5.   three 3   nine 9

6.   __ + __ = 2   __ + __ = 2

Directions:

4. There are 8 rabbits. 5 hop away. How many rabbits are left? Fill in the number sentence.

5. Trace the numbers 3 and 9. Write each number 3 more times.

6. There are different ways to make a sum of 2. Finish the number sentences.

Lesson #29

1.

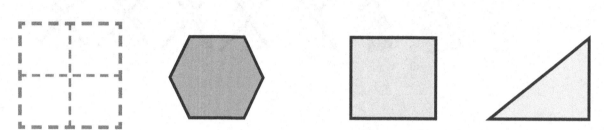

2.

$$4 - 2 = \underline{\hphantom{00}}\qquad 2 - 0 = \underline{\hphantom{00}}$$

$$1 - 1 = \underline{\hphantom{00}}\qquad 3 - 2 = \underline{\hphantom{00}}$$

3.

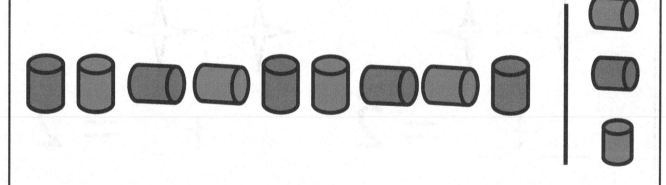

Directions:

1. Trace the dotted lines. What shape can be made from 4 squares? Circle it.

2. Write the differences.

3. Circle the object that should come next in the pattern.

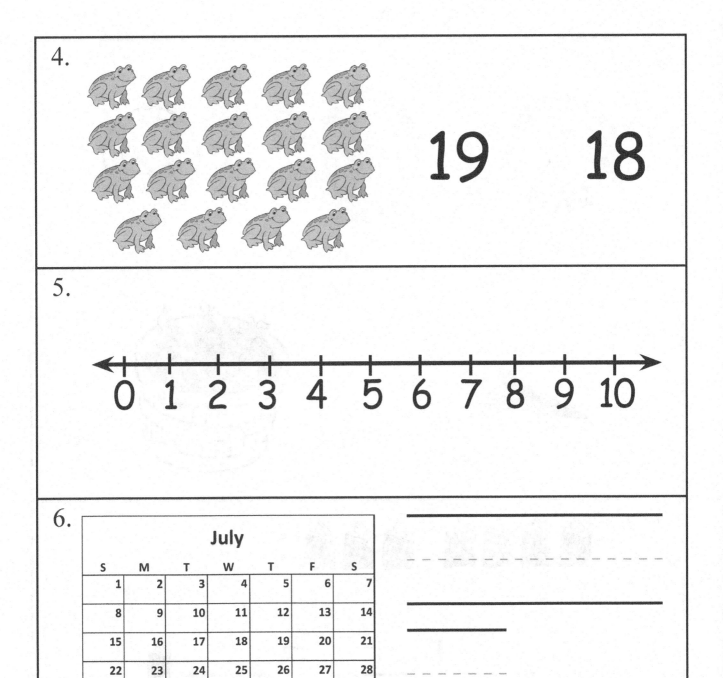

4.

19   18

5.

0 1 2 3 4 5 6 7 8 9 10

6.

July

S	M	T	W	T	F	S
1	2	3	4	5	6	7
8	9	10	11	12	13	14
15	16	17	18	19	20	21
22	23	24	25	26	27	28
29	30	31				

_____ Saturdays

Directions:

4. Count the frogs. How many are there? Circle the number.

5. Circle the number that comes before 5.

6. What month does the calendar show? Write the name of the month. Circle every Saturday. Use a red marker. Write the number of Saturdays.

Lesson #30

1.

2.

3.

$$ \underline{\hspace{2cm}} + \underline{\hspace{2cm}} = \underline{\hspace{2cm}} $$

Directions:

1. Circle the coin that is worth 1¢.

2. Circle the object that is **heavier**.

3. Ben read 4 books over the summer. Ann read 3 books. How many books did they read in all? Fill in the number sentence.

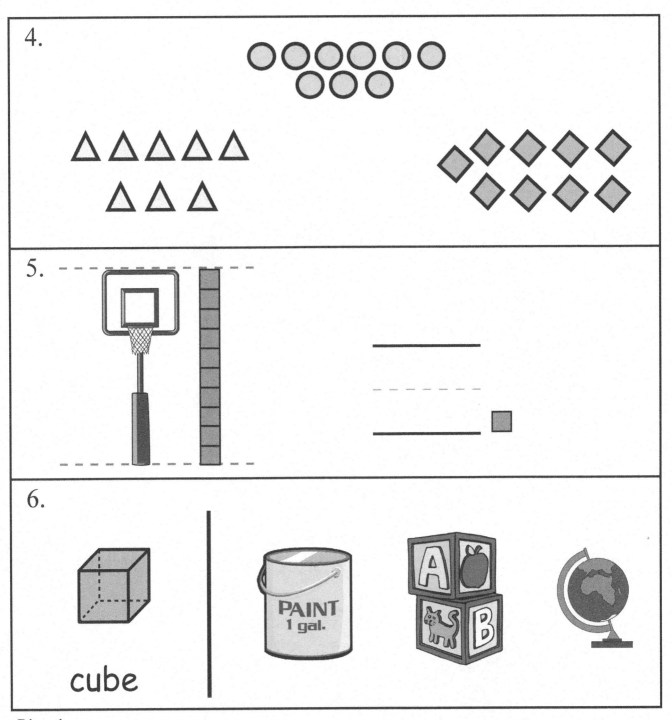

Directions:

4. Count the circles. Which group is **equal to** the group of circles? Circle it.

5. How many squares tall is the basketball hoop? Write the number on the line.

6. Circle the objects that are in the shape of a cube.

Level K

Mathematics
3rd Edition

Help Pages

Help Pages

Numbers

0	zero	
1	one	
2	two	
3	three	
4	four	
5	five	
6	six	
7	seven	
8	eight	
9	nine	
10	ten	

Help Pages

Numbers

11	eleven	
12	twelve	
13	thirteen	
14	fourteen	
15	fifteen	
16	sixteen	
17	seventeen	
18	eighteen	
19	nineteen	
20	twenty	

Help Pages

Comparing

Before / After:

The number that is **before** 3 is **2**.

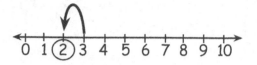

The number that is **after** 6 is **7**.

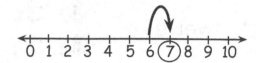

More / Fewer:

There are **5** dogs in this group.

There are **3** monkeys in this group.

This group has **more**.

The number **5** is **more than** (or greater than) 3.

5 is **equal to** 5.

This group has **fewer**.

The number **3** is **fewer than** (or less than) 5.

3 is **equal to** 3.

Longer / Shorter:

The hammer is **longer** than the screwdriver.
The screwdriver is **shorter** than the hammer.

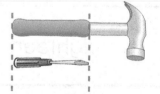

Taller / Shorter:

The lamp is **taller** than the candle.
The candle is **shorter** than the lamp.

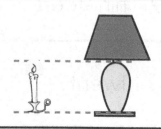

Help Pages

Shapes

2-D shapes: these shapes are flat and can be measured two ways, length and width

Circle	Triangle	Square
Rectangle	Pentagon	Hexagon

3-D shapes: these shapes are solid and can be measured three ways, length, width, height/depth

Cube	Cone	Cylinder	Sphere

Some shapes have corners.

Look at these corners.

Some shapes do not have corners.

Help Pages

Money

 This is a **penny**. It is worth **1¢**.

 This is a **nickel**. It is worth **5¢**.

 This is a **dime**. It is worth **10¢**.

Comparing

A clock has two hands. The long hand is the **minute hand**.
The short hand is the **hour hand**.

The minute hand is pointing to the 12.

On this clock the hour hand is pointing to the 4.

The time is **four o'clock** or 4:00.

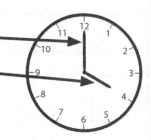

 The time is **nine o'clock** or 9:00.

Help Pages

Calendar

Reading a Calendar:

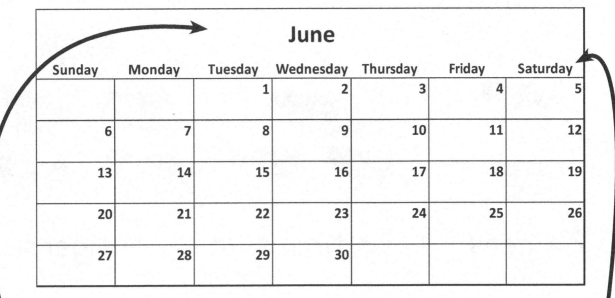

June

Sunday	Monday	Tuesday	Wednesday	Thursday	Friday	Saturday
		1	2	3	4	5
6	7	8	9	10	11	12
13	14	15	16	17	18	19
20	21	22	23	24	25	26
27	28	29	30			

- A calendar tells the **name of the month**. This month is **June**.

- The **days of the week** are on the top of the calendar. There are **7** days in a week. The days of the week are **Sunday, Monday, Tuesday, Wednesday, Thursday, Friday,** and **Saturday**.

- The calendar also tells how many days are in the month. This month has **30** days.

Help Pages

Addition

When you find **how many in all**, you **add**. The plus sign **(+)** tells you to add.

2 tigers   +   3 tigers   =   5 tigers

There are **5 tigers** in all.

1 duck   +   2 ducks   =   3 ducks

There are **3 ducks** in all.

Help Pages

Subtraction

When you find **how many are left**, you **subtract**. The minus sign **(–)** tells you to subtract.

4 apples   –   2 apples   =   2 apples

There are **2 apples** left.

6 bananas   –   5 bananas   =   1 banana

There is **1 banana** left.

Level K

Mathematics
3rd Edition

Answers to Lessons

Lesson #1	Lesson #2
1.	1. $\underline{2} + \underline{1} = 3$ $\underline{1} + \underline{2} = 3$
2.	2. 5 (circles in blue)
3.	3.
4. 5 ¢	4.
5. $\overline{\text{II}}$ o'clock	5.
6. $4 + 0 = \underline{4}$ $2 + 2 = \underline{4}$ $3 + 1 = \underline{4}$ $3 + 2 = \underline{5}$	6. 6 7 $\underline{8}$ 9 10

Lesson #3	Lesson #4
1. 17.⬜	1. 10¢
2. 8 – 1 = 7	2. 16
3.	3. 3 o'clock
4.	4.
5.	5.
6.	6.

Lesson #5	Lesson #6
1. 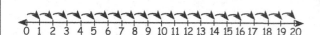	1.   
2. $0 - 0 = \underline{0}$ $4 - 2 = \underline{2}$ $3 - 1 = \underline{2}$ $1 - 1 = \underline{0}$	2. ★★★★★★★ ★★★★★★★ $\underline{5} + \underline{2} = 7$ $\underline{3} + \underline{4} = 7$
3. 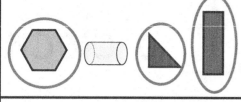	3. 
4. 	4. 
5. 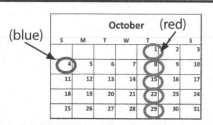	5. 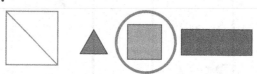
6. 2 3 4 5 6	6. 

Lesson #7	Lesson #8
1. zero 0 / one 1 ● OOOO	1. 10
2.	2.
3. 5¢	3. April / Friday Monday (Saturday)
4.	4. $1+1=\underline{2}$ $2+0=\underline{2}$ $1+3=\underline{4}$ $2+3=\underline{5}$
5. 3	5.
6.	6. 5 o'clock

Lesson #9	Lesson #10
1. 	1. $\underline{\quad3\quad} + \underline{\quad5\quad} = \underline{\quad8\quad}$
2. 	2. two 2 / three 3 2 2 2 2 3 3 3 3
3. 	3.
4. $\underline{3}+\underline{1} = 4 \qquad \underline{2}+\underline{2} = 4$	4.
5. 6¢	5. 0 1 2 3 4 5 6 7 8 9 10
6. 	6.

Lesson #11	Lesson #12
1. 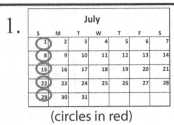 (circles in red)  Sundays — days in a week	1. 
2. 	2. $\underline{3} + \underline{3} = 6$ $\underline{2} + \underline{4} = 6$ $\underline{1} + \underline{5} = 6$
3.  ⑫  14	3. 
4. 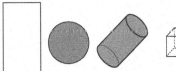	4. 
5. 	5. 10.
6. $3 - 2 = \underline{1}$ $2 - 2 = \underline{0}$ $1 - 0 = \underline{1}$ $4 - 1 = \underline{3}$	6.  

Lesson #13	Lesson #14
1.	1. ___ __8__ o'clock
2. ___6___ – ___2___ = ___4___	2.
3. four 4 5555 4444 five 5	3. $0 + 3 = \underline{3}$ $2 + 1 = \underline{3}$ $1 + 0 = \underline{1}$ $0 + 0 = \underline{0}$
4. cone	4. 15
5.	5. November S M T W T F S 1 2 3 4 5 6 7 8 9 10 11 12 13 14 15 16 17 18 19 20 21 22 23 24 25 26 27 28 29 30 4 Thursdays (circles in red)
6. 0 1 2 3 4 5	6.

Lesson #15	Lesson #16
1. $5+5 = 10$ $6+4 = 10$ $3+7 = 10$	1.
2. 3¢	2.
3.	3. 0 1 2 3 4 5 6 7 8 9 10
4.	4.
5.	5. six 6 6 6 6 6 seven 7 7 7 7 7
6. 0 1 2 3 4 5 6 7 8 9 10 11 12	6.

Lesson #17	Lesson #18
1. $5 - 3 = \underline{2}$ $4 - 4 = \underline{0}$ $2 - 1 = \underline{1}$ $3 - 0 = \underline{3}$	1.
2. 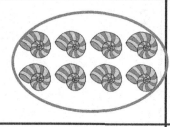	2.
3. 	3.
4. 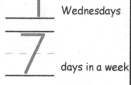 August (circles in green) Wednesdays days in a week	4. 
5. 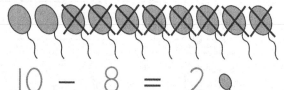 $\underline{10} - \underline{8} = \underline{2}$	5.   $\underline{1} + \underline{4} = 5$ $\underline{5} + \underline{0} = 5$
6. 	6. 

Lesson #19	Lesson #20
1.	1.
2. 6 7 8 9 10	2. 4 + 5 = 9
3. cylinder	3. 8 ■
4. 6 o'clock	4. 1 + 1 = 2 1 + 4 = 5 0 + 5 = 5 1 + 2 = 3
5. eight 8 nine 9 8 8 8 8 9 9 9 9	5. February (red) (blue) 4 Fridays 4 Saturdays
6.	6. 13

Lesson #21	Lesson #22
1.	1.
2.	2. ten 10 five 5
3. 10¢	3.
4. $4 + 5 = 9$ $6 + 3 = 9$ $1 + 8 = 9$	4. 0 1 2 3 4 5 6 7 8 9 10
5. 0 1 2 3 4 5 6 7 8 9 10 11	5.
6.	6.

Lesson #23	Lesson #24
1. 16 (20)	1.
2. $3 - 3 = \underline{0}$ $4 - 3 = \underline{1}$ $3 - 2 = \underline{1}$ $5 - 5 = \underline{0}$	2
3.	3. circle
4. March 4 Mondays (circles in red)	4.
5. 8	5.
6.	6.

Lesson #25	Lesson #26
1. 3 _4_ 5 _6_ 7 _8_	1. 14
2. 12 o'clock	2. $2 + 3 = 5$ $1 + 3 = 4$ $5 + 0 = 5$ $2 + 2 = 4$
3. _4_ + _5_ = _9_	3.
4.	4.
5. $4 + 4 = 8$ $7 + 1 = 8$ $3 + 5 = 8$	5.
6. two 2 eight 8 2 2 2 2 8 8 8 8	6. December (circles in red) _4_ Sundays _7_ days in a week

Lesson #27	Lesson #28
1. ⌐5.	1.
2. (number line 0–19)	2.
3. (pennies) 7¢	3.
4. (shapes)	4. $8 - 5 = 3$
5. (cars)	5. three 3 — 3 3 3 3 / nine 9 — 9 9 9 9
6. (shapes)	6. $1 + 1 = 2$ $2 + 0 = 2$

Lesson #29	Lesson #30

1.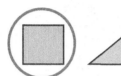

1.

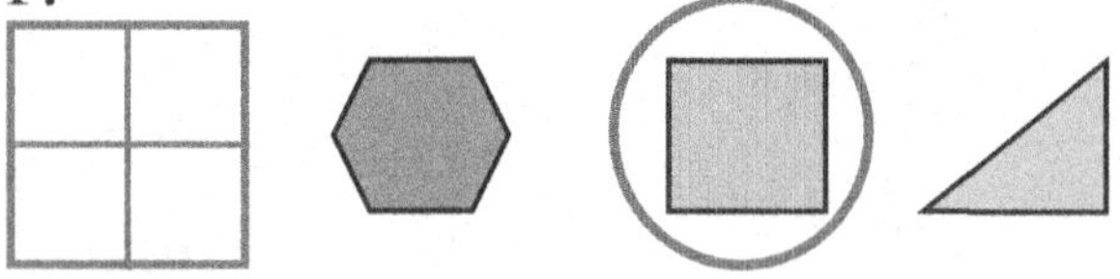

2.

$4 - 2 = \underline{2}$ $2 - 0 = \underline{2}$

$1 - 1 = \underline{0}$ $3 - 2 = \underline{1}$

2.

3.

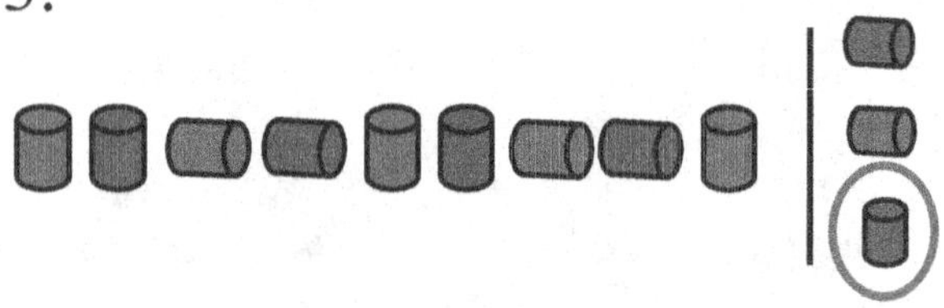

3.

$\underline{4} + \underline{3} = \underline{7}$

4.  (19) 18

4.

5.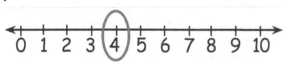

0 1 2 3 (4) 5 6 7 8 9 10

5.

$\overline{10.}$

6.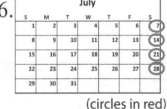

July

S	M	T	W	T	F	S
1	2	3	4	5	6	(7)
8	9	10	11	12	13	(14)
15	16	17	18	19	20	(21)
22	23	24	25	26	27	(28)
29	30	31				

July

4   Saturdays

(circles in red)

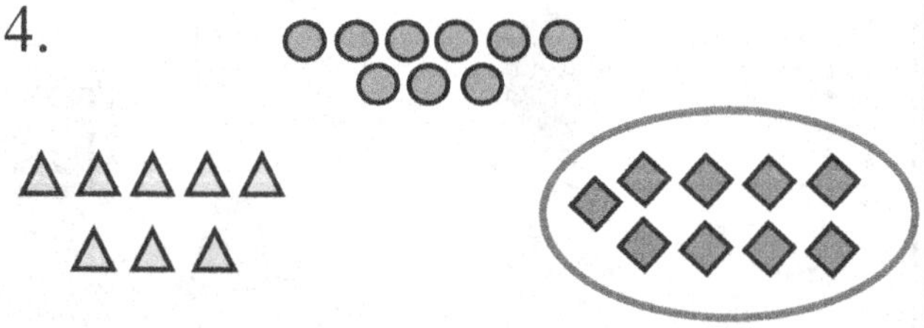

6.

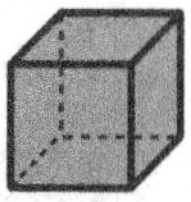

cube